FROG'S LUNCH

Written by Dee Lillegard

Illustrated by Jerry Zimmerman

SCHOLASTIC INC.

New York   Toronto   London   Auckland   Sydney

Copyright © 1994 by Scholastic Inc.
All rights reserved. Published by Scholastic Inc.
Printed in the U.S.A.
ISBN 0-590-27378-7

3 4 5 6 7 8 9 10   09   00 99 98 97 96 95 94

Frog was sitting on a lily pad
in the middle of the pond.
"It's lunchtime," said Frog.

Along came a fly.
"Mmmm, lunch," said Frog.